Ladybird Readers

The Twits

Series Editor: Sorrel Pitts
Text adapted by Rachel Godfrey
Activities written by Catrin Morris
Song lyrics by Wardour Studios

LADYBIRD BOOKS

UK | USA | Canada | Ireland | Australia
India | New Zealand | South Africa

Ladybird Books is part of the Penguin Random House group of companies
whose addresses can be found at global.penguinrandomhouse.com.
www.penguin.co.uk   www.puffin.co.uk   www.ladybird.co.uk

Penguin
Random House
UK

Adapted from *The Twits*,
first published in the UK in 1980
This Ladybird Readers edition published 2021
001

Printed in China

A CIP catalogue record for this book is available from the British Library

ISBN: 978-0-241-36820-6

All correspondence to:
Ladybird Books
Penguin Random House Children's
One Embassy Gardens, 8 Viaduct Gardens, London SW11 7BW

Ladybird  Readers

ROALD DAHL
The Twits

Based on the original title
by Roald Dahl
Illustrated by Quentin Blake

Picture words

Mr. Twit

Mrs. Twit

walking stick

worm

the monkeys

stretch **up** **down**

cage **glue** **upside down**

key **ceiling** **shrink**

The Twits are not nice people.

Mrs. Twit puts worms in
Mr. Twit's food.

"Mrs. Twit's walking stick
is very long now," says
Mr. Twit.

"I'm shrinking!"
says Mrs. Twit.

"You can stretch," says Mr. Twit.

Mrs. Twit goes up.

Then, she comes down.
She is angry.

This is the Twits' house.

Mr. Twit puts glue on
a tree.

He catches birds with
the glue.

The Twits eat the birds.

The Twits have four
monkeys in a cage.

Mr. Twit says to
the monkeys,
"Walk upside down!"

The monkeys are sad.

One day, a beautiful bird
comes to the monkeys' cage.

He says to the birds,
"There's glue on the tree!"

Now, the birds sit on
the cage.

Mr. Twit cannot catch any birds. He is angry.

Mr. and Mrs. Twit go to the shops.

The beautiful bird gets the key. The monkeys open the cage.

The monkeys put glue on
the Twits' chairs and tables.

Then, the birds put the
chairs and tables on
the ceiling.

The Twits come back.

Two birds put glue on
their heads.

The Twits see the chairs and
tables on the ceiling.

"We're upside down!"
says Mrs. Twit.

Mr. Twit says, "Walk upside down."

Mr. and Mrs. Twit have glue on their heads.

They cannot walk.

They shrink.

That is the end of the Twits!

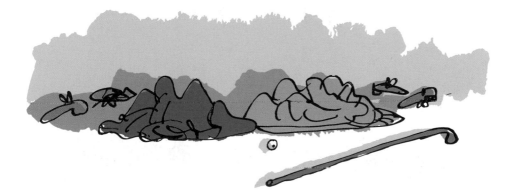

Activities

The key below describes the skills practiced in each activity.

 Spelling and writing

 Reading

 Speaking

 Listening*

 Critical thinking

 Singing*

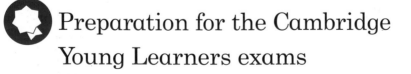 Preparation for the Cambridge Young Learners exams

*To complete these activities, listen to the audio downloads available at **www.ladybirdeducation.co.uk**

1 Match the words to the pictures. 📖

1 Mr. Twit

a

2 Mrs. Twit

b

3 the monkeys

c

4 worm

d

5 bird

e

6 cage

f

2 **Read the words and match them with the correct pictures. Write 1—4.**

1 Stretch.

2 Shrink.

3 It opens things.

4 It is above you in a room.

a

b

_____1_____ ....

c

d

....

3 **Look and read. Put a** ☑ **or a** ☒ **in the boxes.** 📖 ✿

1  This is a cage. ✓

2  These are birds. ☐

3 This is a walking stick. ☐

4  This is a worm. ☐

5 They are upside down. ☐

4 Find the words.

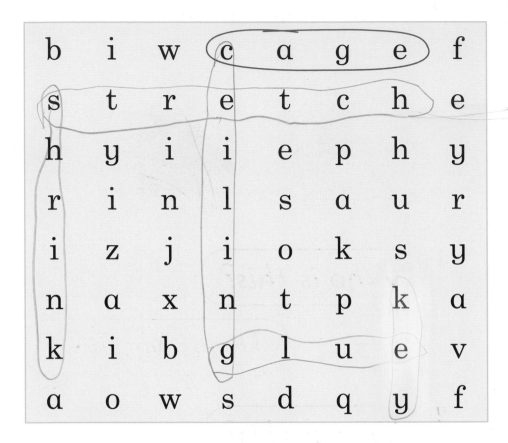

```
b   i   w   c   a   g   e   f
s   t   r   e   t   c   h   e
h   y   i   i   e   p   h   y
r   i   n   l   s   a   u   r
i   z   j   i   o   k   s   y
n   a   x   n   t   p   k   a
k   i   b   g   l   u   e   v
a   o   w   s   d   q   y   f
```

cage

ceiling

glue

key

shrink

stretch

5 **Work with a friend.**
Talk about the pictures.

1 Who is this?

This is Mr. Twit.

2 Who is this?

This is . . .

3 Are they nice people?

Yes, / No, they . . .

6 **Look at the pictures. Look at the letters. Write the words.**

1   u l g e

g l u e

2   n l i i g e c

3   t t s h r e c

4   k o y e m s n

5   h s n k i r

7 **Complete the sentences.
Write a—d.** 📖

1 Mrs. Twit puts worms ....C........

2 The Twits have ....a........

3 Mr. Twit puts glue ....

4 Mr. Twit catches ....

a four monkeys in a cage.

b birds with the glue.

c in Mr. Twit's food.

d on a tree.

8 Circle the correct pictures. 📖 ❓

1 It can open things.

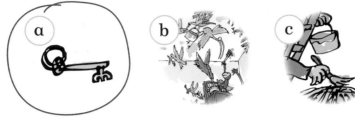

2 She is coming down.

3 They are on a cage.

4 They are upside down.

9 Write *angry*, *sad*, *long*, or *nice*.

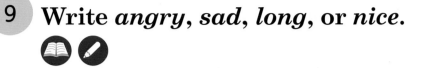

1  The Twits are not
___nice___ people.

2  "Mrs. Twit's walking stick
is very _____ now,"
says Mr. Twit.

3  Mrs. Twit is _____.

4  The monkeys are

_____.

10 **Read the questions.**
Write the answers.

1 Who are the people in the picture?

They are Mr. and Mrs. Twit.

2 Are they nice people?

....

3 Which animals are in the picture?

....

4 What do Mr. and Mrs. Twit want
them to do?

....

11 **Circle the correct words.**

1 The monkeys put glue on the Twits'
  a arms   **b** chairs
    and legs.   and tables.

2 Then, the birds put the chairs and
  tables on the
  a ceiling.   **b** floor.

3 The Twits come
  a back.   **b** house.

4 Two birds put glue on their
  a feet.   **b** heads.

12 **Write the correct sentences.**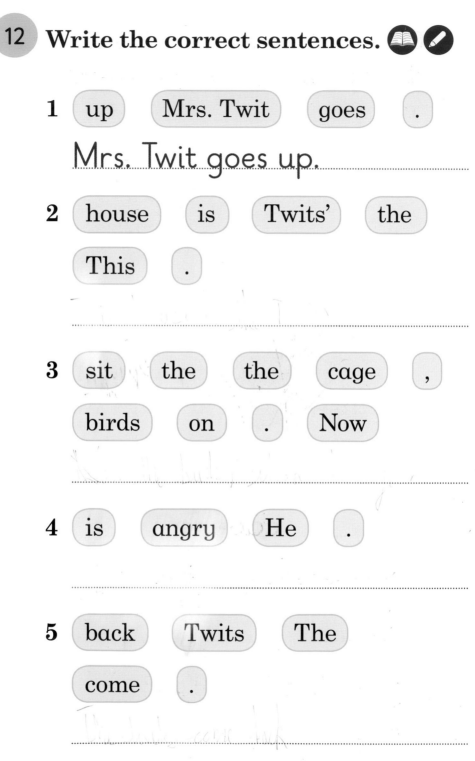

1 (up) (Mrs. Twit) (goes) (.)

Mrs. Twit goes up.

2 (house) (is) (Twits') (the)

(This) (.)

....

3 (sit) (the) (the) (cage) (,)

(birds) (on) (.) (Now)

....

4 (is) (angry) (He) (.)

....

5 (back) (Twits) (The)

(come) (.)

....

13 **Look at the picture and read the questions. Write one-word answers.** 📖 ✏️ ⭐

1 Where are the monkeys?

In a _____cage_____.

2 Who is helping them?

A beautiful _____.

3 What does the bird get?

The _____.

14 **Match the words.**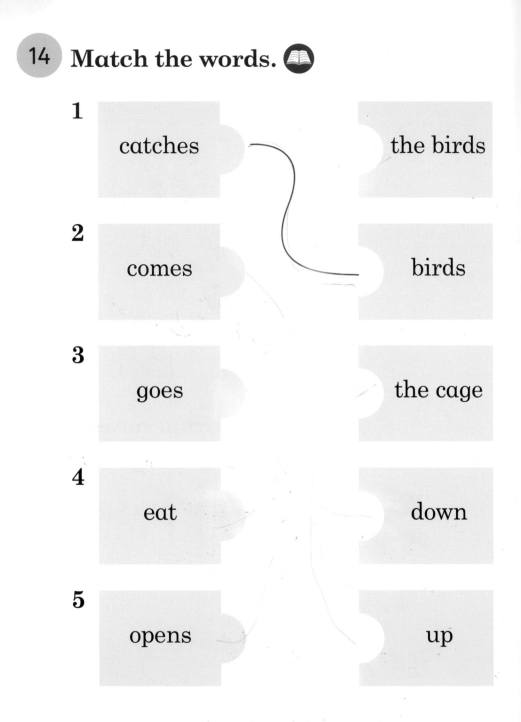

1   catches   the birds

2   comes   birds

3   goes   the cage

4   eat   down

5   opens   up

15 **Look and read. Write *on* or *to*.**

1 One day, a beautiful bird comes
_____ to _____ the monkeys' cage.

2 He says _____ the birds,
"There's glue _____
the tree!"

3 Now, the birds sit _____
the cage.

4 Mr. and Mrs. Twit go
_____ the shops.

16 **Listen, and write the answers.**

1 Where do the monkeys put the glue?

On the chairs and tables.

2 Where do the birds put the chairs and tables?

....

3 What do the birds put on the Twits' heads?

....

4 Who is upside down?

....

17 Order the story. Write 1—4. 📖

.... A beautiful bird helps the monkeys.

___1___ Mr. and Mrs. Twit are not nice to the monkeys.

.... Mr. and Mrs. Twit shrink.

.... The monkeys put glue on the Twits' tables and chairs.

18 Ask and answer the questions with a friend.

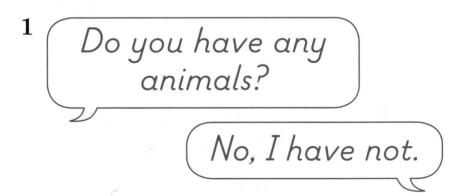

1 Do you have any animals?

No, I have not.

2 What is your favorite animal?

3 Which is your favorite animal in the story?

4 Do you like Mr. and Mrs. Twit?

19 Sing the song. 🎵

The Twits are not nice people.
They catch birds with glue.
A beautiful bird comes to their house—
What do the birds and monkeys do?

The Twits, the Twits,
They are not nice—they are bad.
The Twits, the Twits,
They make the birds and monkeys sad!

The monkeys open the cage.
The monkeys play and the birds fly!
They catch the Twits with glue . . .
Then the Twits shrink—goodbye!

The Twits, the Twits,
They are not nice—they are bad.
The Twits, the Twits,
Now the birds and monkeys are not sad!

Visit www.ladybirdeducation.co.uk
for more FREE Ladybird Readers resources

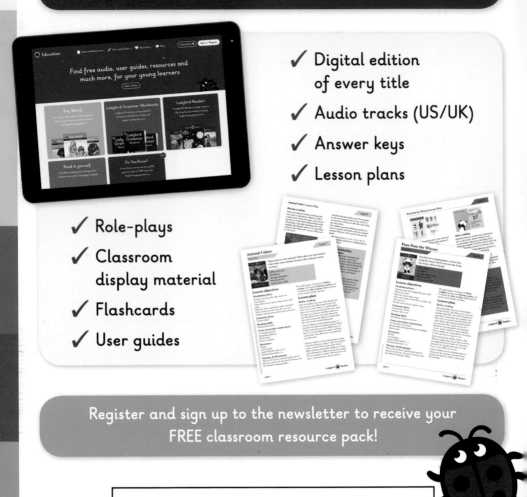

✓ Digital edition of every title
✓ Audio tracks (US/UK)
✓ Answer keys
✓ Lesson plans

✓ Role-plays
✓ Classroom display material
✓ Flashcards
✓ User guides

Register and sign up to the newsletter to receive your FREE classroom resource pack!

To access the audio and digital versions of this book:

1 Go to www.ladybirdeducation.co.uk
2 Click "Unlock book"
3 Enter the code below

h3W6MFLTUB